The
Match
From
HELL!

a play

Tony Norman

Illustrated by
Paul Savage

Warrington
& Vale Royal
College

...Where reading happens

✈ **DARK FLIGHT**

Titles in Dark Flight

Fast Food Nightmare	Stan Cullimore
Robot Girlfriend	Stan Cullimore
Steel Eyes	Jonny Zucker
Skateboard Power	Jonny Zucker
Code Breakers	Jillian Powell
5010 Calling	Jillian Powell
Terror World	Tony Norman
The Match From Hell	Tony Norman
Something Evil	David Orme
Space Wreck	David Orme

Badger Publishing Limited
Oldmedow Road,
Hardwick Industrial Estate,
King's Lynn PE30 4JJ
Telephone: 01438 791037
www.badgerlearning.co.uk

The Match From Hell!   ISBN 978 1 84424 495 9

2 4 6 8 10 9 7 5 3

Text © Tony Norman 2005
Complete work © Badger Publishing Limited 2005
Second edition © 2014

Series Editor: Jonny Zucker
Publisher: David Jamieson
Editor: Paul Martin
Design: Jain Birchenough
Cover illustration: Paul Savage

The Match From *HELL!*

Tony Norman

Contents

NOTE: All the action takes place in the Allstars' dressing room, at Silver Park.

Characters

Bill Peters - coach of Silver Park Allstars under-15s

Ryan - hard centre-back

Lee - ace winger

Aaron - top striker

Suggsy - brave keeper

Callum - midfield moaner

Scene 1:
15 minutes before

Sunday morning. The Silver Park Allstars are getting ready for a Cup semi-final. They sit around chatting, as they put their kit on.

Ryan

See United last night, Suggsy?

Suggsy

Brilliant!

Callum

So lucky.

Ryan

How can three-nil be lucky?

Callum

The first one was off-side for a start.

Suggsy

Just 'cos City lost!

Callum

That ref was a joke.

Ryan

Can't see you laughing.

Suggsy

He never does.

Ryan

No, he just moans.

*Team Coach Bill Peters walks over.
He sees the boys talking and thinks
they are getting on well.*

Bill

That's right guys, let's talk about it.
We're gonna win today. This Cup's
got our name on it.

Suggsy

We kick off at eleven, don't we?

Bill

That's right, Suggsy.

Suggsy

Where are they all then?

Bill

You tell me. (*Bill looks worried.*)

Callum

Luke's not coming for a start.

Bill

Why not?

Callum

He heard you had him down as sub.

Suggsy

Thrown a moody, has he?

Callum

Big time.

Bill

How many times do I have to tell you lot? It's a squad game these days.

Callum

He wanted to start the game.

Ryan

That's his problem. Who needs him?

Bill

Well... we do. He was the only sub.

Callum

Bad news.

Ryan

You love all this, don't you?

Callum

It does help if you have a team.

Ryan's mobile rings. He answers.

Ryan

Hello?... What?... I can't... You keep breaking up.

Bill

Who is it?

Ryan

Lee.

Callum

Bet he can't play.

Suggsy

Hey, shut it.

Ryan shouts into his phone.

Ryan

WHERE ARE YOU?... Oh no!

Bill

What?

Ryan

He got cut off.

Callum

Nice one.

Bill

Why do I bother? It's always the same with this team. Life's one big soap opera.

Ryan

He said they're on the way.

Bill

But where are they now?

Ryan's mobile bleeps. He reads the text out loud.

Ryan

It's from Aaron. He's with Lee. They thought we were playing away today.

Bill

At River Oaks?

Ryan

Yeah. They're waiting for a bus.

Callum

We've lost.

Ryan and Suggsy

SHUT IT!

Bill walks away with his head in his hands....

Scene 2:
5 minutes before

The nine Allstars players sit listening to Bill's team talk.

Bill

We can do this guys. Okay, it's a bit of a test....

Callum

A bit?

Bill

A lot of teams play great when they're down to ten men.

Callum

Yeah, but we've only got nine.

Ryan

We've only got eight.

Bill

What?

Ryan points at Callum.

Ryan

You can't count that loser.

Bill

Cut it out you two.

Callum

You're the loser, Ryan.

Ryan jumps to his feet.

Bill

Hey! I said cut it out! If we don't stick together, we've got no chance.

Ryan sits down.

Bill

Look guys, Lee and Aaron are on the way. We just need to hold out 'til they get here. Stay cool guys. That's all you've got to do. Just stay cool....

Suggsy

Yeah, we can do this. Just keep it tight.

Bill

That's right. I want four in midfield, four at the back, and Suggsy in goal. You'll keep them out, won't you mate?

Suggsy

I'll do my best Bill.

Bill

That's all I'm asking any of you to do.

Callum

I don't believe you lot. This is a joke.

Ryan

No, you're the joke, you dweeb!

The referee sticks his head around the dressing room door.

Referee

Ready?

Bill

Yes ref, we're on the way. Come on guys, let's really go for it.

The Allstars run out of the dressing room. Most of them look keen, but Callum still looks very moody.

Scene 3: Half-Time

The team troop back into the dressing room. They all look tired and fed up.

Callum

I told you, it's a joke.

Bill

Come on guys, we're only two down.

Ryan

Only thanks to Suggsy. It could be six.

Bill

Yeah, well played Suggsy. You kept us in it son.

Callum

What's the point? We've got no chance.

Ryan's mobile rings. He pulls it out of his sports bag and answers.

Ryan

Lee? Where are you?... No, you've got to be joking! Lee?... Hey!

Bill

Well?

Ryan

It was Lee.

Callum

We know that much.

Ryan

They can't make it.

Bill

What?

Suggsy

Why?

Ryan

He didn't say. He rang off.

Callum

The Match From Hell. That's what this is, The Match From Hell.

Nobody argues with Callum. The dressing room goes very quiet. Then the door flies open. Lee and Aaron run in smiling. Lee points at Ryan.

Lee

Got ya!

Ryan

Very funny.

Bill

It's no joke lads.

Lee

Look, sorry we're late.

Aaron

We've had a nightmare.

Callum

No, we've had the nightmare.

Ryan

Playing out there with nine men.

Lee

What's the score?

Suggsy

Two-nil.

Aaron

We'll get it back.

Callum

You'd better.

Ryan

Yeah, like you tried so hard in the first half Callum.

Callum

What d'you want me to do?

Ryan

Try running for a start

Bill claps his hands.

Bill

Hey! I told you two before. Cut it out.

Ryan and Callum glare at each other.

Bill

Right, Lee and Aaron, get changed.
The rest of you, well done. Good first
half. You did well. Now we've got a
full team, let's go out and win it.

*Most of the team agree with Bill. The
mood of the Allstars is on the up.*

Scene 4: Last minute

The dressing room door bangs open. Ryan storms in and kicks his sports bag across the room. Bill comes in. He looks very angry too.

Ryan

No way! There's no way he should have sent me off.

Bill

It wasn't a foul. You won the ball.

Ryan

We get back to two-all, then he gives a soft penalty like that!

Bill

I know Ryan, I know.

Ryan takes his boots off and throws them at the wall.

Bill goes to the open door to see what's happening out on the pitch.

Bill

They're still talking to the ref.

Ryan

Won't do any good.

Bill

It never does. Anyway, the ball's on the spot now. Their big striker's taking it. He shoots and...
WELL DONE SUGGSY! BRILLIANT SON!

Ryan

He saved it?

Bill

Yeah! He's kicked it up to Lee on the wing…. They're wide open at the back. COME ON LEE, GET YOUR CROSS IN! Lovely ball. Come on Aaron, hit it first time…. YES! GOAL!!!

Ryan runs to the door and stares out at the pitch. The ref blows for full time.

Ryan

That's it. We've done it. We're in the Final!

Ryan and Bill run out to greet the rest of the team.

Scene 5: 5 minutes after

The Allstars are back in the dressing room. They all have big grins on their faces.

Ryan

Well played Callum... in the second half.

Callum

Not bad for a dweeb.

They both smile. Suggsy is at the dressing room door.

Suggsy

Look at this. Bill's having a real go at the ref.

The players run over and look out of the door. Bill storms back in.

Ryan

What was that all about?

Bill

I told him he should never have sent you off. I said you could miss the Final thanks to him.

Ryan

What did he say?

Bill

He said you won't, but I will.

Suggsy

Why?

Bill

He wants to ban me!

All the players laugh. Suggsy does
a good take-off of Bill's voice.

Suggsy

Stay cool guys. That's all you've got
to do. Just stay cool....

Ryan

It's always the same with you Bill.
Life's one big soap opera!